G000166950

Roderick Hunt

Comprehension plus

BOOK 1

FOREST GRANGE SCHOOL

Contents

A day at the zoo	2
Alphabet game	4
Trapped!	6
A man's best friend	8
The toyshop	10
A game to play	12
The sports shop window	14
Order please	16
A good cup of tea	18
A day at the seaside	20
Signs of the times	22
Caring for your dog	24
Captain Barney's houseboat	26
The village of Popton	28
Whatever next	30
Find the pairs	32
It's a frog's life	34
Parrot Island	36
Litter, litter, litter	38
Who did it?	40
London	42
Games	44
Make a finger puppet	46

Oxford University Press

A day at the zoo

Rod, Helen, and Valerie spent a day at the zoo. If you look at the plan you will see where they went.

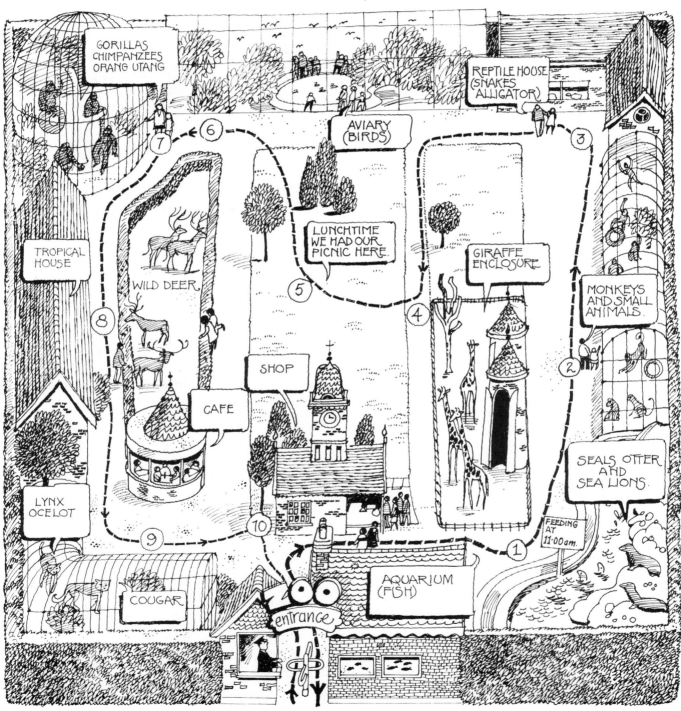

The keepers at Dublin Zoo had a tricky problem. How could they keep their two gorillas happy in the long evenings? The gorillas kept fighting or attacking their cage because they were bored. Gorillas are intelligent animals. In the wild they live in large families. There is always something to look at or to do. In a zoo it is different. There was not much to do in their cage.

In the end, the zoo found the answer. They gave them a television. Now the gorillas sit and watch it quite happily. They like cowboy films best.

A Look at the plan of the zoo on the opposite page and finish these sentences.

1 First the children saw the . . .
2 Then they looked at the . . .
3 Next they went into the . . . and saw the . . .
4 After that they walked down to the . . .
5 By then it was . . . so they had their . . . on the . . .
6 After lunch they went to . . .
7 They went to the . . . next.
8 Then they visited the . . .
9 They took a quick look at the . . .
10 Last of all they called at the . . . to buy their . . .

B What are these?

1 It lives in Africa. It looks like a horse. It has a thick mane. It has black and white stripes.
2 It comes from South America. It has brightly coloured feathers. It has a hooked beak. It can learn to talk.
3 It lives on river banks. It has long jaws with sharp teeth. It has a long scaly body with a strong scaly tail.
Make up some more of your own.

C Answer these questions about the story at the top of this page.

1 Why were the keepers worried about their gorillas?
2 What had the gorillas been doing?
3 How do gorillas live when they are not in zoos?
4 What was different about being in a zoo?
5 How did the zoo solve the problem?

D Here are some animal sounds that have been muddled up. Give each animal the right sound.

snakes	grunt
wolves	chatter
hippopotamuses	howl
monkeys	roar
lions	hiss

E Talk about zoos using the following points to help you.

1 Have you ever been to a zoo? Which zoo was it? What did you like about it?
2 How is a wild life park different from a zoo. Which do you think is better?
3 Do you think that it is cruel to keep wild animals in cages, or are animals in zoos contented and well looked after?

3

Alphabet game

The seaside can be fun on a nice sunny day, but it can also be dangerous. The children in this picture are in great danger.

A **Look at the picture of the seaside on the opposite page.** You will find at least one thing starting with each letter of the alphabet. See if you can list them all. Some are harder than others.

B **There are lots of things beginning with the letter S in the picture.** One is 'sea'. Try to find ten more.

C **Copy this word cross. Then fit the letters of the word ALPHABET into it using the clues to help you.**

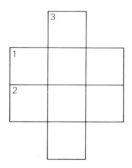

A L P H A B E T

Across 1 A vegetable found in a pod.
2 A short way of saying laboratory.

Down 3 To make something hot.

D **Answer these questions about the picture of the two children in the plastic dinghy.**

1 How can you tell that the children are a very long way from the shore?

2 Why do you think the children are so far out to sea?
3 Why do you think people are waving at them?
4 Why are they in danger?

E **Here are Kate's things. Kate made a list of them in alphabetical order. See if you can write out the list in the same order.**

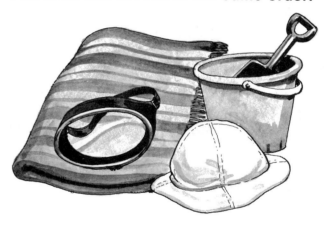

F **Something to talk about**

1 Talk about other seaside toys that can be dangerous.
2 Most people in the picture opposite are having fun and being sensible, but two things are happening where people are being foolish and doing dangerous things. Which are they?
3 Make up an alphabet game using cars or animals, or things in your classroom.

Trapped!

PETER

ALAN

Two boys spent six uncomfortable hours trapped in a disused warehouse. Peter Jones, 8, and Alan Green, 9, decided to explore the warehouse yesterday afternoon. The boys were trapped when the steel door of the cold-store room shut behind them. They were rescued when a policeman heard the boys' dog barking. 'It was thanks to my little dog, Spot,' said Alan. 'He was in the store-room with us. After we couldn't shout any more Spot just went on barking.' A search party that was about to start looking for the boys was called off.

A Look at the picture of the two boys on the opposite page and answer these questions.

1 Which boy do you think is a cub scout?
2 One boy fell off his bicycle recently. Which do you think it was?
3 Where do you think Alan went for his holiday last year?
4 What is one of Peter's interests?
5 Which boy owns the dog?
6 Why might you think that Peter wants a new watch for his birthday?

B Draw a 3 x 3 square and fill it in using the clues given below.

1		
2		
3		

1 Female is to *girl* as male is to _____
2 It comes before *two*.
3 The opposite of no.

Now draw another grid and try these clues:
1 You can drink tea from it.
2 A broken lightbulb is no _____
3 You may use it when you write.

C Look at the story of how Alan and Peter were trapped in a warehouse and answer these questions.

1 How old are the two boys?
2 How did they become trapped in the cold-store room?
3 How do you know that their parents knew that they were missing?
4 How did the boys try to get help?
5 How did the policeman find the boys?

D Here is a description of Peter. Copy it out putting the right words in the spaces.

Peter Jones is of average height for his age. He is well-built. He has a round face with freckled cheeks. He has fair, _____ hair and blue eyes. His front _____ is broken. He is wearing blue denim _____, a roll-neck _____ and a bomber jacket. On his feet he has a pair of _____.

E Something to talk about.

1 If someone went missing you would have to describe them. Think of someone in your family. Can you describe what that person was wearing this morning?
2 Try covering the opposite page with a book. Then see if you can remember:
   a Which boy is wearing trainers?
   b What is hanging from Peter's belt?
   c What is the difference between the two boys' watches.
   Make up some more memory test questions and try them on your partner.

A man's best friend

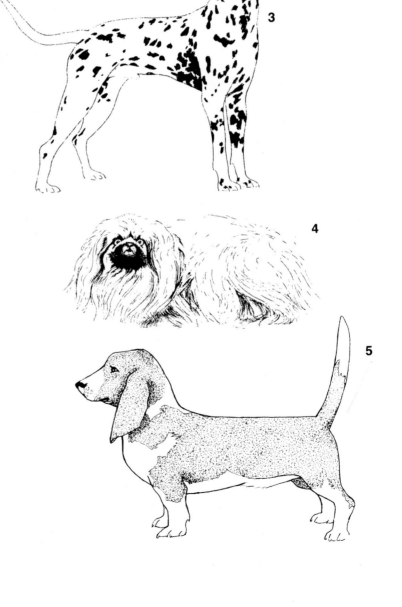

The Pekinese. When these dogs were kept in China 2,000 years ago they were known as lion dogs. The Pekinese is very small with long hair that reaches almost to the ground. Its face is flat and looks squashed.

The basset-hound. This dog is very good at following a scent. It has a smooth coat with black, white, and brown markings. It has long, floppy ears and a sad-looking face. It has short legs, a long powerful body and a long pointed tail.

The dachshund. This dog is sometimes called the sausage dog because of its very long, thin body and short legs. It was once used to hunt badgers because it is a good shape to go down a badger hole to drive the badger out.

The Dalmatian. Because of its white coat with black spots, this dog is known as the 'spotted dick' or 'plum pudding dog'.

The greyhound. No breed of dog in the world can run as fast as the greyhound. It has a strong lean body with a short smooth coat. Its legs are very long. It has a long tail, and a long neck with a small head and pointed muzzle.

8

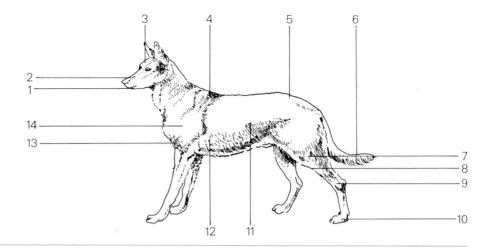

1 Jaws
2 Muzzle
3 Stop
4 Withers
5 Croup
6 Tail
7 Upper thigh
8 Stifle
9 Lower thigh
10 Foot
11 Flank
12 Ribs
13 Forechest
14 Shoulder

A Look at the pictures of the dogs on the opposite page. Which dog is which?

Write down numbers 1–5 and put the correct name of the dog by each one.
Now answer these questions.

1 Which breed of dog is the fastest in the world?
2 Like all hounds the basset is good at what?
3 Why do you think the Pekinese was called the lion dog?
4 Why was the dachshund good at hunting badgers?

B Here's how to change *dog* to *fox* by changing one letter at a time:

dog   fog   fox

Now change *man* to *dog* using the clues below.

m a n
dog

a small rug to go on the floor

you wear this on your head

very, very warm

you put this over the letter i

Now try these: *cat* to *pet*, *dog* to *cat*, *pet* to *dog*

C Look at the points of a dog at the top of this page and answer these questions.

1 What is the name of a dog's side?
2 What is the part called where the neck joins the back?
3 What do we call a dog's mouth and nose?
4 Where is a dog's *shoulder*?
5 Where on a dog is the *stop*?

D Talk about dogs as pets using these points to help you.

1 Why do you think a dog is such a good pet?
2 People say 'The dog is man's best friend'. What do you think this means? How do some dogs help people?
3 Dogs are intelligent animals. How well would you say they can think for themselves?

E Here is a chart which shows how many children in one class have pets.

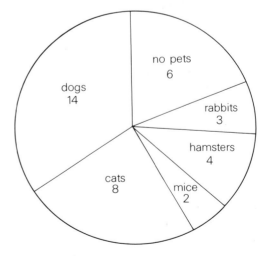

1 Which pet is the most popular?
2 Find out how many children in your class or group have a pet. Make a list of them and draw a pie chart or bar graph to show them.

The toyshop

The big surprise

One Christmas there were so many toys and presents to give to a family of three children that their father decided to surprise the children by putting the presents in a huge wooden box. The box was so big that the children needed a small step ladder to see inside it.

Once the children had opened all the presents they put them aside and spent the rest of Christmas playing with the big wooden box.

A Look at the toys from the toyshop and answer these questions.

Games	Soft toys	Models and kits

1 Copy the headings Games, Soft toys, Models and Kits, and discuss some of the toys. Then write some of them in under the right headings, as shown above.
2 What sort of toys do you like best?
3 What would you choose as a small present to take to a party or to put in a stocking.
4 Can you spot the toys to which each of these belong.

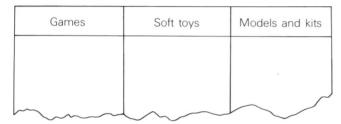

a

b

c

d

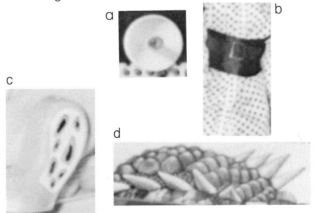

B Draw a 4 x 4 square grid and fit in the correct words across from the list below.

car   pram   bus   toy
top   bike   kit   ball

1		P	▨
2		L	
3		A	
4		Y	▨

C Read the story at the top of this page and answer these questions.

1 What did the children's father do with the huge wooden box?
2 Why did the children need a step ladder?
3 What did the children do for the rest of Christmas?
4 How might the father have been surprised by what the children did?
5 Why did the children like playing with the wooden box?

D Something to talk about.

1 Do you think that children need lots of expensive toys to keep them happy?
2 Do you think that children today watch too much television and don't play enough?

A game to play

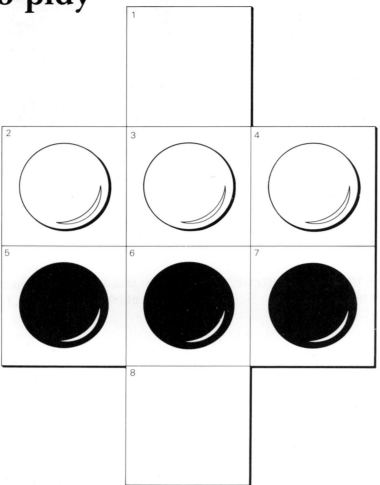

Here's a board game you can make.

Make the board by copying the eight squares, as shown, on card or stiff paper.

Make three white counters and three black counters. Place them on the board in the positions shown.

The game is to get the white counters where the black counters are and the black counters where the white counters are.

Here are the rules.

First you must move a white counter, then a black counter, and so on, in turn.

You can move in any direction – backwards, forwards, sideways or diagonally, but only one square at a time.

You must always move to an empty square.

What is the smallest number of moves you can do it in?

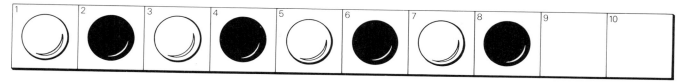

Here is another game you can try. Make four white counters and four black counters. (If you find it hard to cut circles, cut out squares and snip the corners off.) Place the counters in a row as shown. The game is to get all the white counters together and all the black counters together in four moves.

Here are the rules.
For each go you move any two counters that are next to each other, e.g. 1 and 2, or 6 and 7 (NOT 1 and 3). You must move the two counters together and you must not change them round as you move.

A **The two games on these pages are all about changing positions. Change the position of these words to make sensible sentences.**

1 cow moon the jumped over the
2 this market pig went to little
3 sing song sixpence of a
4 a Miss little sat tuffet on Muffet.

B **Fit the letters given into the word cross to make five words using the clue down to help you.**

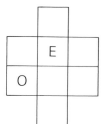

S S A A T T

Clue down – It's what you sit on.

Here is another one for you to try:

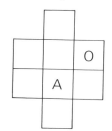

B K O O T T

Clue down – You row it or sail in it

C **The groups of sentences below are muddled up. Write them out in a sensible order.**

The elephant	which you drink through a straw	changes colour when it gets wet.
The fizzy drink	which has red and pink stripes	needs a crane to lift it.
The lady's swimsuit	which wobbles on a plate	tastes cool and refreshing.
The big jelly	which weighs two tons	has a blob of cream on top.

D **Something to talk about.**

Kate, Sam and Ann had to go to the dentist. 'You go first,' said Kate to Ann. 'No let Sam go first,' said Ann. 'I'm not going first,' exclaimed Sam. 'I'm going last.' While they were waiting, they lined up in six different ways. Here are two of the ways:

Kate   Sam   Ann

Kate   Ann   Sam

What other ways could they have lined up?

The sports shop window

People have always enjoyed playing ball games. This picture was painted on the wall of a tomb in Egypt over 4,000 years ago. Games rather like football and bowls also go back for thousands of years. Clubs or sticks for hitting balls were used in early versions of hockey and cricket.

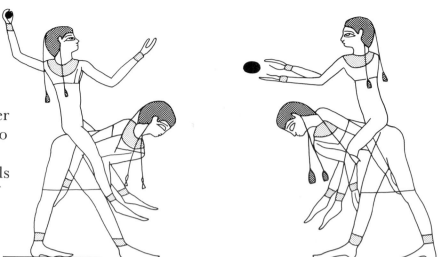

A Look at the sports shop window and write down the names of:

1 Three sports that use a bat or a racket.
2 One sport that is played on a table.
3 Two sports that take place on or in water.
4 Three sports that are played by teams.

B Here are some items that are used in sport. Write down the number of each one, and next to it write its name.

1   2   3   4   5

golf ball   football   tennis ball
shuttle cock   cricket ball
   e.g. 1 – tennis ball

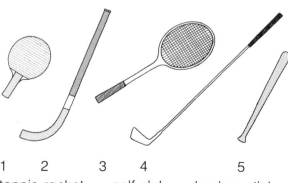

1   2   3   4   5
tennis racket   golf club   hockey stick
rounders bat   table tennis bat

C Look at the information at the top of this page and answer these questions.

1 What sort of game are they playing in the picture?
2 What sort of early game do you think would be played with stone balls?
3 What other games can you think of which use a stick or bat to hit a ball?

D Write down the odd-one-out in each list.

1 Shorts, track suit, sweat shirt, singlet, netball.
2 Tennis racket, ice skates, cricket bat, snooker cue, hockey stick.
3 Tennis, cricket, fishing, rounders, football.

E Something to talk about.

1 Some sports you play by yourself, some you play in a team, some you play against one other person. Think of some of each kind to talk about.
2 Which sport do you enjoy watching most on television. Which one do you not enjoy seeing?
3 Which sport do you think you might like to play when you grow older?
4 Talk about the items in the sports shop window on the opposite page. Do you know the names of all the sports for which they are used.

Order please

After a hard day's work, Mr Mothersole is on his way home.
He lives at number 126. But the pictures are in the wrong order.

1

2

3

4

5

Make a dancing man

You need about twelve pieces of card 5cm × 4cm. Put the cards in a pile and start with the last one. On each card draw a little man near to the right-hand edge. The man should be about $2\frac{1}{2}$cm high to perform best. Change him slightly each time you draw him. Staple the cards together on the left-hand side to make a little book.

If you flick the pages very quickly with your right thumb, the man will seem to dance.

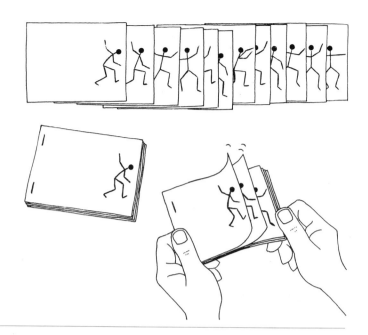

A Look for clues in each picture on the opposite page to help you put them in the right order. Write down the numbers in the order you think they should be.

B Write out each list of words in a sensible order.

1 night, afternoon, morning, evening.
2 grown-up, baby, teenager, child.
3 July, June, August, May.
4 dinner, breakfast, supper, tea.
5 Tuesday, Thursday, Wednesday, Monday.
6 today, yesterday, next week, tomorrow.

C Draw a 4 x 4 square grid as shown and fit the words across from the list below.

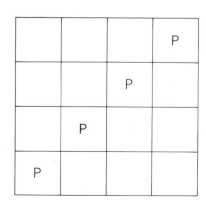

drop   open   pens   rope

D These sentences, about having a meal, are in the wrong order. Copy them out putting them in the right order.

We sat down and ate it all.
Then we fried some eggs.
First we cooked the bacon.
We served the bacon and eggs with fried bread.
It tasted delicious.

E Put these sentences in the right order and write them in your book, giving the first word a capital letter.

1 mat cat the on sat the.
2 drink good milk to is.
3 wrong to lies tell is it.
4 sun the is sky in the.
5 always careful be the road crossing.

F Something to talk about.

1 How are books arranged in a library? Why is it sensible to put the books in order?
2 How is the food arranged in a supermarket? Why is it sensible to arrange it like this?
3 What sort of order would it be sensible to use in doing the following?
   making a sandwich
   washing up the dinner things
   washing your hair
   cleaning your shoes

17

A good cup of tea

1 Switch on the kettle.

2 Set the tray with 3 cups.

3 Pour some milk into a jug.

4 Pour some hot water into the pot to warm it, and then empty it.

Boiling water can be very dangerous. Never boil water unless a grown-up thinks it is safe for you to do so.

5 Put 3 spoons of tea into the pot.

6 Pour in the boiling water.

7 Wait 3 minutes for the tea to brew.

8 Enjoy a good cup of tea.

A Look at the pictures of how to make a cup of tea and answer these questions.

1 What do you do first?
2 What can you do while the kettle is on the boil? (pictures 2 & 3)
3 For what do you use a little of the hot water?
4 How much tea do you use?
5 What do you do when the kettle has boiled?
6 How long do you let the tea brew?

B Draw a 3 x 3 square grid and fill in the words across using the clues given.

1		
2		
3		

1 A good cup of _____.
2 It's what you hear with!
3 What _____ little girls made of?

C Look at the information at the top of this page and answer these questions.

1 Why should you never hold the teapot when you fill it with boiling water?
2 Why should you never pour towards you?
3 Why should you keep the pot away from the edge of the table?
4 What may happen to you if you lift the lid of a boiling kettle?
5 How could you safely refill a kettle that has just boiled?
6 Why is it best to carry a teapot on a tray?

D Here are four lists of words all to do with making a cup of tea. Write down the odd word out in each list.

1 cup, saucer, kitchen, spoon, teapot.
2 milk, butter, tea, sugar, water.
3 hot, cold, warm, boiling, wet.
4 boil, stir, wash, pour, brew.

E Something to talk about.

1 Talk about jobs you do to help out at home. Do you have certain jobs to do or do you just help sometimes?
2 Talk about how you would do *one* of these:
   clean your teeth
   set the table for a meal
   look after felt-tip pens

A day at the seaside

These are the photographs that Kerry took when she went to the seaside with her class.

Here is a page from Kerry's notebook.

Our Beach Survey

Here are some of the shells we found

MUSSEL - black and shiny, two halves on a hinge

LIMPET - Cone shaped, clings to rocks

SCALLOP - large, flat, rounded, with ridges down it.

WHELK - fat, spiral shell

RAZOR - long and flat with square ends

TOP SHELL - small cone-shaped and slightly rounded.

A Look at the photographs that Kerry took.

You can see that Kerry has put them in order ready to stick into her folder. She will write a few words under each one.
1 What do you think she will write under picture 1?
2 What do you think she will write under picture 6?
3 What do you think she will write under picture 3?
4 What do you think she will write under picture 2?

B Here are the words that Kerry wrote under each photograph, but they are all mixed up. Write them out in the right order.

Playing rounders on the sand
Finding a crab
Doing a beach survey
Visiting the lighthouse
Stopping on the way
Drawing a picture

C Look at the page from Kerry's notebook.

Each drawing of a shell has a number by it. Use Kerry's notes to decide what the shells are. Write down the numbers with the name of each shell beside them.

D Draw a 5 x 5 square grid and write in the word SHELL as shown. Then fill in the squares across using the clues below.

¹S				
²	H			
³		E		
⁴			L	
⁵				L

1 A fish _____ in the sea.
2 The land along the edge of the sea.
3 At the seaside it's nice to have an ice_____.
4 Small fish swim in little _____ in the rocks.
5 In rock pools you will also find _____ fish.

E Something to talk about.

1 Talk about a school or class trip that you have been on, or one that you are planning.
2 Imagine your teacher has asked you to suggest a good place for your class to visit. Talk about one or two places and say why you think it would be good to go there.
3 Why is the seaside an interesting place to visit?

Signs of the times

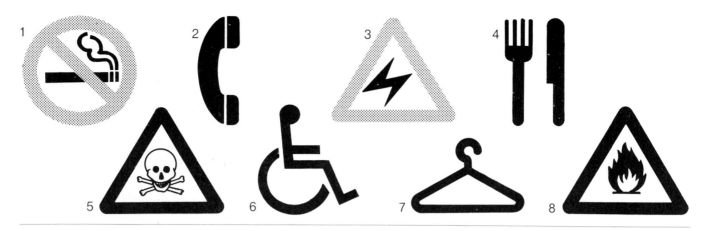

A Look at the picture of the street on the opposite page and answer these questions.

What does this tell motorists NOT to do?

What does this sign mean?

What king is this?

Which shop has this sign?

What does this sign mean?

Where do you see this sign? What does it stand for?

B Draw a 4 x 4 square grid. Copy in the letters as shown. Work out which words from the list fit in across.

	R		
		U	
			R
		I	

king   blue   boar   cafe   free   bank

C Look at the symbols at the top of this page. Can you tell what they mean? Copy out the list and put the right number next to each meaning.

fire danger
cloakroom
disabled persons
danger zone
no smoking
electricity danger
a place where food is served
you can phone from here

D Debbie has designed two signs for the classroom to show something that is allowed and something that is forbidden.

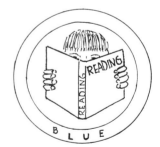

Design a sign like Debbie's. Here are some ideas:
    books should be tidy
    no eating sweets in the classroom
    remember to water the plants

E Something to talk about.

There are all kinds of signs, notices and posters in the streets and roads. Talk about some which you have seen.

Caring for your dog

Make sure you never tease your dog.

Don't leave your dog shut up for long periods.

Make sure your dog has plenty of exercise.

Practise every day what you want your dog to learn.

Teach your dog to 'sit' and 'stay'.

Teach your dog to come when you call.

Don't feed your dog 'tit bits' from the table.

Teach your dog to go to his basket and stay there when told.

Train your dog to walk on a lead without pulling.

Keeping a pet

Most people like the idea of having a pet, but they don't always stop to think how much time and care an animal needs, especially if it is young.

Every year people give up keeping a puppy. They find they just haven't time to train their new pet and take it for walks. This is not very fair on the young puppy.

A **Answer these questions about how to care for a dog.**

1 Why do you think it is a bad thing to tease a dog?
2 How can you let a dog know when he has done well or been good?
3 What may happen to a dog that doesn't get enough exercise?
4 Why is it important that a dog comes when you call him?
5 Why should a dog be taught to 'sit' and 'stay'?
6 If you feed a dog 'tit bits' when you eat, what may he do whenever you have food?

B **A young dog is called a *puppy*. Here is a list of animals and a list of their young. They have been muddled up. Match the correct adult animal to its young.**

bear	calf
hen	kid
pig	chick
swan	piglet
goat	cub
cow	cygnet

C **Answer these questions about the information on keeping a pet at the top of this page.**

1 What do people find out after they have had a puppy for a short time?
2 Why do you think it takes a lot of time to look after a very young puppy?
3 Why do you think it is not fair for someone to give up keeping their puppy?

D **Copy out this story about a dog, putting the words from the list in the right spaces.**

splash   pond   duck   fly   silly

I have a little dog called Flop. Flop can be very _____. One day he chased a _____. The duck flew into the middle of a muddy _____. Flop thought he could _____ too, and landed with a _____ in the water.

E **Talk about keeping an animal.**

1 Talk about your own pet, or talk about an animal you would like to keep if you could. How do they need to be looked after?
2 Why is it easy to keep an animal like a dog or a cat, but not one like a snake or a monkey?

Captain Barney's houseboat

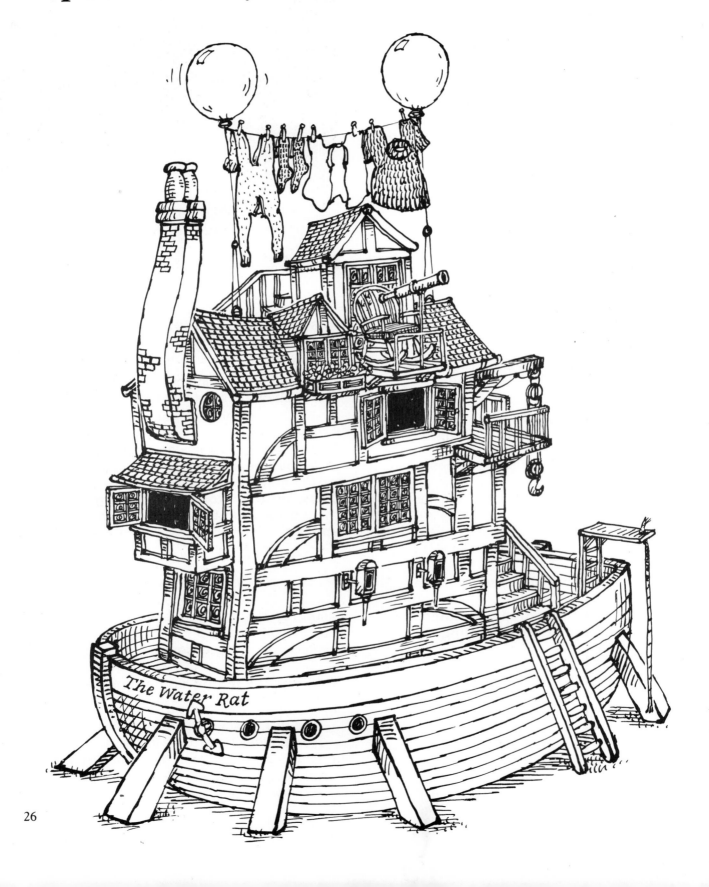

The Triangular Lodge

This strange-looking house has only three sides. The rooms inside are also three-sided.

The house was built almost four hundred years ago. It stands in the grounds of Rushton Hall in Northamptonshire. Of course, nobody lives in it.

A **Answer these questions about Captain Barney's Houseboat.**

1 How can you tell that Captain Barney's houseboat never goes to sea?
2 How can you tell that Captain Barney didn't use any plans to build his house?
3 How does Captain Barney reach the ground in an emergency?
4 How can you tell that Captain Barney likes to spend most of the day in his lookout?
5 How many floors does the houseboat have?
6 What does Captain Barney use to hang up his washing?

B **Draw this 5 x 5 square grid and fill in the words using the clues to help you.**

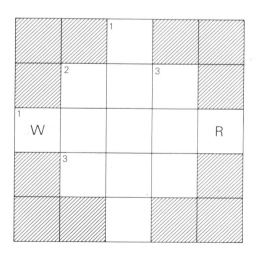

1 We drink it fresh, and fish swim in it.
2 A long-tailed animal with sharp teeth. It looks like a large mouse.
3 The number of toes, or fingers, you have.

C **Answer these questions about the three-sided house.**

1 About what date was the three-sided house built?
2 What sort of furniture would you need to go in the rooms of the house?
3 Why would it be hard to live in three-sided rooms?
4 What is the best shape for rooms to be?

D **In this story about Captain Barney, some of the words are mixed up. Write out the story putting the words in their right places.**

Captain Barney sat on his gas cooker and put a fried egg to his eye. 'My old parrot is coming to tea,' he said. 'Why, I can see him coming now with his friend on his shoulder. I'll cook him a telescope on my rocking chair.'

E **Here is a description of a house. See if you can draw what it says.**

The house has a flat roof. The top of the wall in front looks like a castle battlement. The door has an arched top. On either side of the door is a window shaped like a diamond.

F **Something to talk about.**

Which one of these would you choose for a home? Say which one you'd like and which one you'd hate.
an old lighthouse
a castle
a house under the ground
a giant doll's house
a cottage in the forest

The village of Popton

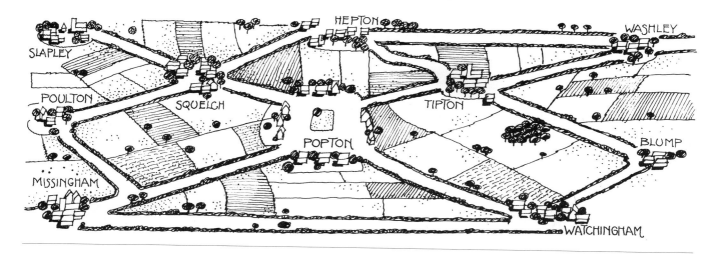

A Answer these questions about the village of Popton.

1 Who lives directly opposite Mrs Merry?
2 Who lives directly opposite Mr Guzzle?
3 Who lives directly opposite Mr Snooze?
4 Who live on either side of Mr and Mrs Sniff?
5 Who lives on the right of Mrs Merry?
6 Who lives on the left of Miss Glum?

B Imagine a clock with hands. Mr and Mrs Sniff live at 12 o'clock.

1 Who lives at six o'clock?
2 Who lives at nine o'clock?
3 Who lives at one o'clock?

C Draw a 4 x 4 square grid. Copy in the letters as shown. Work out which words from the list fit in across.

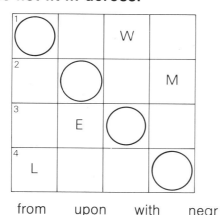

over   from   upon   with   near
down   left   back

You will find the name of someone from Popton in the circled squares.

D Look at the map of North Uppshire at the top of this page. Answer these questions.

1 Which villages have only two roads leading into them?
2 Which villages have four roads leading into them?
3 If you went from Popton to Squelch and turned left, which village would you come to?
4 If you went from Washley to Tipton and turned right, which village would you come to?
5 If you went from Watchingham to Missingham and turned right which village would you come to?
6 Start at Missingham and go to Popton. Turn left. At the next village go right. At the next village go right. Continue straight on. Where do you end up?

Talk about the village of Popton.

E 1 What sort of person do you think Miss Tidy is? How do you think she keeps her house and garden? Why might Miss Tidy not like living next door to Mr Snooze?
2 What sort of person do you think Mrs Merry is? Why might she not like living next door to Miss Glum or Mr Drat?
3 Why might Mr and Mrs Whisper not like living next door to Mr and Mrs Crashem?
4 Make up stories about some of the other people in the village and their names.

Whatever next?

Cuthbert Cuss was too lazy to nail down his stair carpet. One day he tripped over it and fell downstairs. Look what happened next.

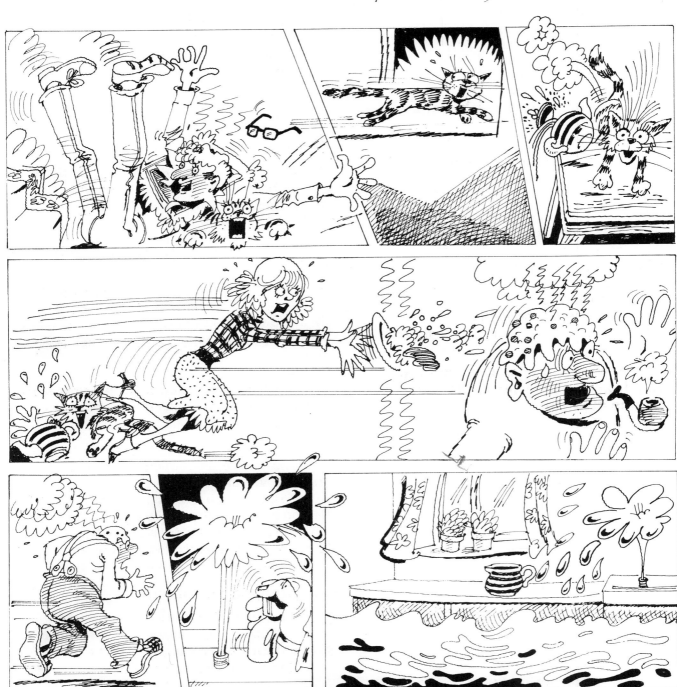

A Answer these questions about the pictures on the opposite page.

1 What happened as Cuthbert Cuss landed at the bottom of the stairs?
2 Where did the cat go?
3 What did the cat do?
4 What happened to Cuthbert Cuss's wife?
5 What happened to the dinner?
6 What did Grandpa do?
7 What happened to the tap?
8 What happened to the kitchen?
9 What do you think happened to Cuthbert?

B Draw the word cross shown. Put in the letters from the sentence underneath it using the clues to help you.

CATS   HARDLY   SPIT

Down

1 Salt and vinegar flavour in a packet?

Across

2 If at first you don't succeed, _____ again.
3 It goes on top of a teapot or saucepan.
4 What you are left with after a fire.
5 A word that means suitable.

C Look at the picture at the top of this page.

What do you think is going to happen next? Could more than one thing happen and how could one thing lead to another? Talk about the picture and work out some ideas. Then tell a story about it.

D These sentences have been muddled up. Write them out putting the right parts together.

Grandpa couldn't eat his toast
  because there were weeds growing on it.
The man fell off the chair
  because it was stuck to the table.
He couldn't pick up the glue pot
  because his false teeth were broken.
The man decided to dig his garden
  because the leg had fallen off.

E Something to talk about.

1 What do people mean when they say that something was a *calamity*?
2 Have you ever had a 'calamity'? Have you ever fallen in a pond, or trodden on the toothpaste? Talk about your calamity.

31

Find the pairs

You can't have one without the other

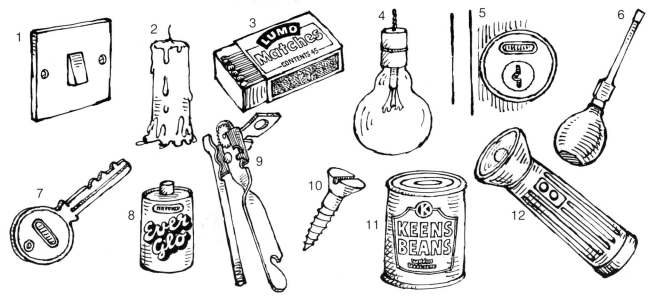

A **Look at the picture of the men and women on the opposite page. Answer these questions.**

1 What is person number 1 doing?
What number is that person's partner?
2 What is person number 2 going to do?
What number is that person's partner?
3 Where is person number 5 working?
What number is that person's partner?
4 What instrument is person number 6 playing?
What number is that person's partner?
5 From what country does person number 7 come?
What number is that person's partner?

B **Here are some pairs of opposites that have been muddled up. Match them up correctly.**

black	far
big	down
wet	white
up	shut
open	small
near	dry

C **Draw a 3 x 3 square grid and fill it in using the clues and letters given.**

O   O   N   N   E   E   E   W   W

1		
2		
3		

Clues

1 It comes before two
2 At this moment
3 A female sheep

D **Look at the pictures at the top of this page. Each one has a partner that it can't do without.**

Work out what the pairs are and write down the numbers putting them together.
e.g. 5 goes with 7

It's a frog's life

A frog's life has three stages.

How the tadpole becomes a frog is the story of one of nature's most amazing changes.

The female lays the spawn in the water. As she does so the eggs are fertilized by the male frog.

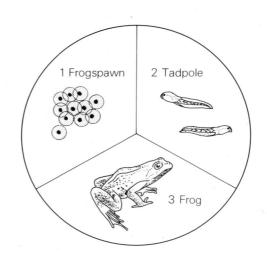

1 Frogspawn 2 Tadpole 3 Frog

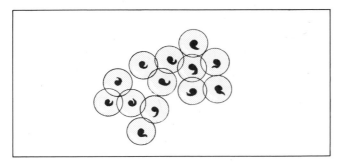

1 The eggs are covered with jelly. As the tadpoles grow they feed on this jelly.

2 The tadpoles leave the jelly and cling on to weeds or plants.

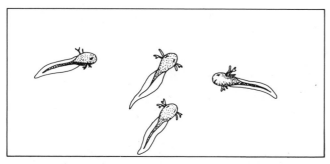

3 Tadpoles breathe through gills like a fish. Soon they leave the plants and swim about.

4 Gradually the tadpole changes. It starts to grow legs. It begins to develop lungs.

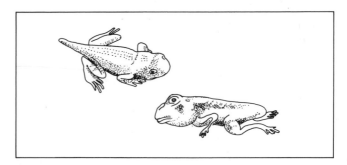

5 During these changes it comes up to the surface to breathe air with its lungs. Its tail shrinks. It loses its gills.

6 At last the tadpole changes into a tiny frog and leaves the water.

How to tell a frog from a toad

	Frog	Toad
skin	smooth and damp	dry and warty
head	long and narrow	short and broad
body	slim-waisted	short and squat
hind legs	usually long	short
movement	hops	crawls or walks
spawn	clustered	ribbons

A Look at the information about frogs and tadpoles on the opposite page and answer these questions.

1 What are frog's eggs called?
2 Where do the very young tadpoles go?
3 What are gills for?
4 How does the tadpole begin to change?
5 Why do the tadpoles need to come to the surface?
6 When do the tadpoles lose their gills?

B Make the word *IN* grow by adding one letter at a time. Use the clues to help you.

1 It flows from a pen.
2 Where people skate.
3 When thirsty you need a . . .

				I	N	
			1	I	N	
		2		I	N	
3				I	N	

Now try this one.

1 It could prick you.
2 To whizz round and round.
3 Your backbone.

				I	N	
			1	I	N	
		2		I	N	
3				I	N	

C Look at the way to tell a frog from a toad at the top of the page. Then copy out the sentences putting the words from each list in the right spaces.

1 dry   smoother   warty   damper

A frog's skin is much _____ and _____ than a toad's skin which is _____ and _____.

2 broader   slim-waisted   squat   short

The frog is _____ _____ but the toad's body is _____ and _____. The toad's head is also much _____.

3 hopping   longer   walks   crawls

The frog's legs are _____ than the toad's, and it moves by _____. The toad _____ or _____.

D Something to talk about.

1 Talk about the three stages of a frog's life. See if you can explain each stage to a partner, or someone in your group.
2 See if you can remember the difference between a frog and a toad. Explain the difference to someone in your group.

35

Parrot Island

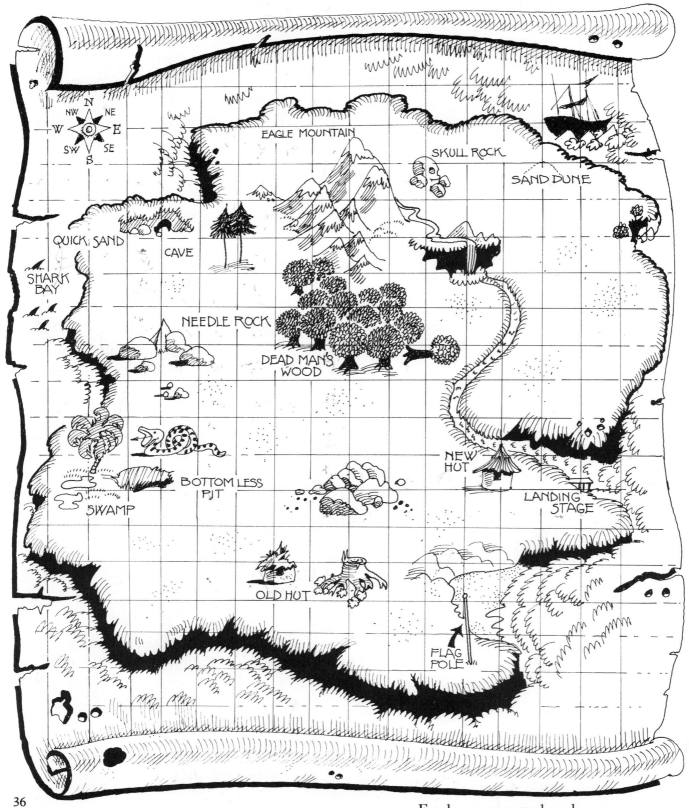

Each square = 1 pole

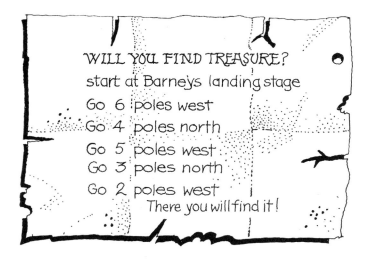

WILL YOU FIND TREASURE?

start at Barneys landing stage

Go 6 poles west
Go 4 poles north
Go 5 poles west
Go 3 poles north
Go 2 poles west
There you will find it!

WILL YOU FIND TREASURE?
Start at the old hut.

Go 2 poles East.
Go 2 poles North.
Go 4 poles North again.
Go 2 poles East.
Go 3 poles North.
Go 2 poles North again.
Go 3 poles East.
There, dig!

A **Look at the map of Parrot Island. Imagine you were shipwrecked and had to live there.**

1 Why would it be best to live in the new hut?
2 Which places would be dangerous to visit?
3 Say why these places would be dangerous.
4 Why would you need a lot of wood?
5 Why might you need a little boat or canoe?
6 If you wanted to be rescued, how could you tell a ship that you were there?

B **This torn-up message was found in a book in the new hut. Can you read what it says?**

TREAS
IN OLD
MAP OF
HIDDEN
LOOK UNDER
URE
HUT
THE FLOOR

C **Look at the instructions at the top of this page for finding treasure.**

Each square on the map opposite measures one pole. E.g. if you start at the landing stage and go 6 poles west you come to the pile of rocks.

1 Follow the instructions for both routes and see where you end up.
2 Which route is a trap?
3 Think of a place to bury treasure on the island and make up some instructions like those at the top of this page. Ask your partner to follow your route. Then try and follow your partner's.

D **Here is the treasure chest. See if you can work out what was found inside it.**

E **Something to talk about.**

1 What sort of things would you find in a pirate's treasure chest.
2 Why do you think people buried treasure?

Litter, litter, litter

Here is a machine for picking up matches, cigarette ends, and litter. These are the parts of the machine: a car, a big wooden drum, a barrel of sticky gum, the seat of an old chair, a look-out tower, some bins.

A **Look at the picture of the litter machine and answer these questions.**

1 What is pushed along in front of the car?
2 How does the drum pick up the litter?
3 How does the gum get on to the drum?
4 What does the man sitting on the bonnet of the car do?
5 What are the men in the tower doing?

B **Draw a 6 x 6 square grid and complete the crossword using the clues given below.**

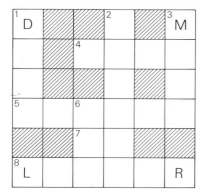

Across

4 If there is no bin, take your litter _____.
5 Sweets are often wrapped in them.
7 Always throw your litter _____ the bin.
8 Waste paper and rubbish left lying around.

Down

1 Do not _____ your litter in the street.
2 A short space of time, only a few seconds.
3 Rubbish and litter make a nasty _____.
6 A hole dug in the ground to put rubbish in.

C **Look at the picture at the top of the page and answer these questions.**

1 How can glass bottles be dangerous if they are left on the ground?
2 How are old cans harmful to animals?
3 How can plastic bags be harmful to animals?
4 How else does litter spoil the countryside?

D **Talk about the problem of litter.**

1 Why is it wrong to throw paper bags or sweet papers on the ground?
2 What problems do these cause as litter – plastic bags, glass bottles, aluminium and tin cans, polystyrene cups, polythene bottles, uneaten food?
3 Is all litter rubbish, or could some of it be used if it were collected carefully?
4 Can you think of any ways to keep the towns and the countryside tidy?

Who did it?

Some valuable silver was stolen from number 77 Duke Street
  by someone who called at the house.
The thief dropped a silver box on the way out.
On the box were three fingerprints.

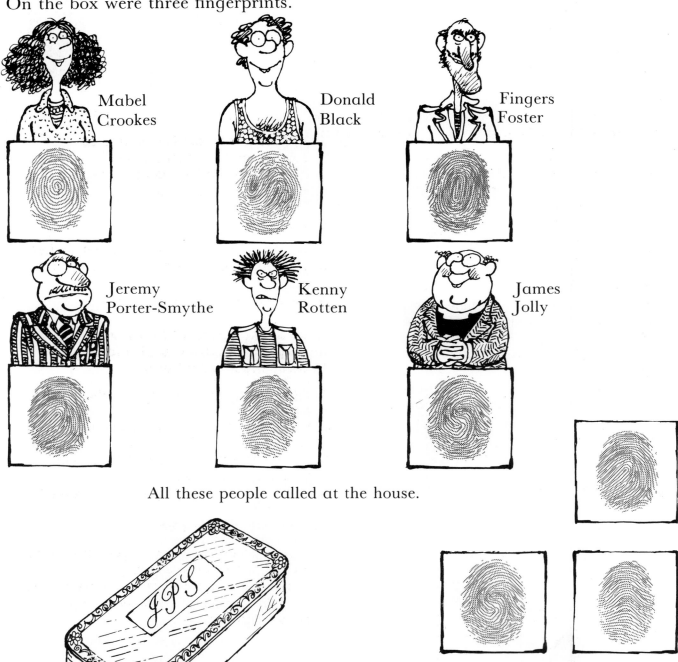

Mabel
Crookes

Donald
Black

Fingers
Foster

Jeremy
Porter-Smythe

Kenny
Rotten

James
Jolly

All these people called at the house.

The silver box.

The fingerprints found on the box.

If you look at your fingertips you will see tiny ridges on the skin. The ridges form a pattern. This pattern makes a fingerprint. Every human being leaves fingerprints. No two fingerprints are exactly alike. No one has fingerprints the same as anyone else in the world. You leave your fingerprints on almost every object that you touch.

There are four main types of fingerprint.

The arch

The whorl

The loop

The mixed

A Look at the fingerprints on the six people on the opposite page and answer these questions.

1 Write the names of the three people who have touched the box.
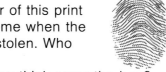
2 The owner of this print was in Rome when the box was stolen. Who is he?
3 Who do you think owns the box?
4 Who do you think stole the box?
5 The thief is wearing clothes that he stole from the man who owns this fingerprint. What is the man's job?

6 The owner of this fingerprint is the detective who caught the burglar. Write down the detective's name.

B Copy this 6 x 6 square grid and complete the crossword using the clues.

Across

1 Your hand has four fingers and one _____.
3 You can make a print with it!
5 Fingerprints are tiny ridges in the _____.
6 From head _____ toe.

Down

2 You can shake, clap, wash, and hold them.
3 Your hand has fingers, your _____ has toes.
4 You can wear it on your finger.

C Look at the information about fingerprints at the top of this page. Answer these questions.

1 What can be seen on every person's fingertips?
2 How many of your own fingerprints are exactly the same?
3 What is the amazing fact about all the fingerprints in the world?
4 How many types of fingerprint are there?

D Something to talk about.

1 Look at one of your own fingerprints. See if you can tell what type it is.
2 Talk about how detectives are able to solve crime by looking for fingerprints on objects to do with the crime.

London

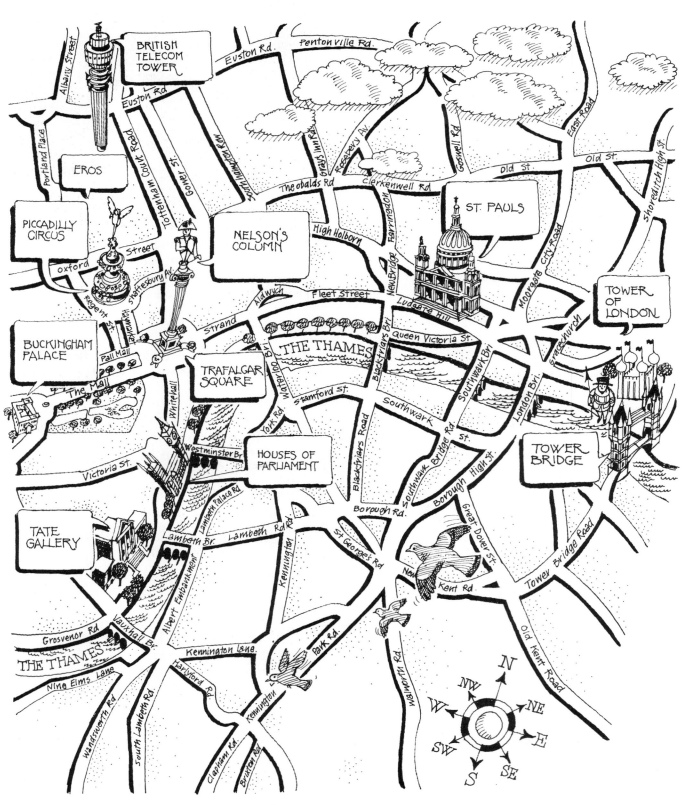

London, capital of the United Kingdom, is the fourth largest city in the world (after Shanghai, Tokyo, and New York). Once it was the largest. It is an old city. There was a town there in Roman times, nearly 2,000 years ago. The oldest part of London is the area called 'The City', where you can find the Tower of London and St. Paul's Cathedral. Many years ago the City was the whole of London but today it is just a small part of it.

A **Look at the map of London on the opposite page and answer these questions.**

1 What stands in Trafalgar Square?
2 Which road leads down to Buckingham Palace?
3 The Houses of Parliament are next to which bridge?
4 Where is the statue of Eros?
5 What happens when tall ships pass under Tower Bridge?
6 Which river runs through London?

B **Copy this 6 x 6 square grid and complete the crossword using the clues below.**

Across

1 Hyde _____ Corner.
3 The capital of the United Kingdom.
4 The oldest part of London is the _____.
6 The West _____.

Down

1 Buckingham _____.
2 The _____ of England.
5 An old-fashioned way of saying *you*.

C **Answer these questions about the information on London at the top of this page.**

1 Which city is the largest in the world?
2 How long ago were the Romans in Britain?
3 What is the oldest part of London?
4 Which two buildings can be found in The City?

D **Something to talk about.**

1 Talk about somewhere interesting you have been to in a big town or city.
2 Where will you choose to live when you grow up – in a big town, a small town, or in the country?
3 Do you like living where you are at present? Would you like to live somewhere else?

Games

A **Wizzword** by Milton Bradley
Challenge each other to unscramble mixed-up words. Can you be first with the solution, press the button, and leave your opponent in a confusion of letters? Claim his letters! You've won the first round.
Age 8 upwards. Two players.

J 10   Wizzword

B **Yahtzee** by Milton Bradley
Your strategy will depend on how your first throw of the five dice turns out. Five of a kind? Yahtzee! Well done, you get maximum points. But if your luck is out, you can still win by skilful play.
Age 8 upwards. Two or more players.

J 11   Yahtzee

C **Operation** by Milton Bradley
Become a doctor. Operate on the patient and remove a knee cap, or an ankle bone. But beware. One slip with the tweezers and the buzzer sounds.
Age 6–14 years. Two to four players.

J 12   Operation

D **Stay Alive** by Milton Bradley
Be the last player with marbles on the board. Players need skill and quick wits to move the plastic slides. These open the holes that will let an opponent's marbles drop through.
Age 7 upwards. Two to four players.

J 13   Stay Alive

E **Battleship** by Milton Bradley
Sink your opponent's ships before he sinks yours. The well-made playing cases allow the game to be played at home or while travelling.
From 8 years to adult. Two players.

J 14   Battleship

F **Watch It!** by Milton Bradley
Use any six cards to make a picture, then sit back as your opponents race to repeat it from memory. Was the dog on the left or the right? Was it a house or a windmill? Getting it right isn't easy and your turn is next.
Age 5–12 years. Two to four players.

J 15   Watch It!

Simon

Simon says . . . repeat my sequence of lights and sounds exactly. Each time the sequence is longer and gets more difficult. Who can meet Simon's challenge and carry on longest to win? Three ways to play. Requires batteries.

Grandstand Astro Wars

Defend your earth ships against a fierce invasion. You must dodge the enemy missiles and fire back at the attacking fighters, warships, and enemy command ships. If you survive you can attempt the exciting docking manoeuvre and earn extra points. Requires batteries or mains adaptor.

A **Look at the games on the page opposite and write answers to these questions.**

1 In which game are marbles used?
2 In which game do the players throw dice?
3 Write down the names of two games where you need a steady hand.
4 In which game do you need a good memory?
5 In which game do the two players use a square grid?
6 In which game do players have to be good at spelling?
7 Of all the games on the page, which one would you like to play most of all? Say why.

B **Copy this 6 x 6 square grid and complete the crossword using the clues given below.**

Across
1 It's what you play.
4 The middle four letters of 'gloves'.
6 The opposite of difficult.
7 You take a _____ when you go one after the other.

Down
1 The winner's medal may be made of this.
2 In some games the players make a _____.
3 Your opponent is the other _____.
5 If you work, you may _____ money.

C **Look at the pictures of the games at the top of this page and answer these questions.**
1 How does playing Simon get more difficult as you go on?
2 What does a player have to defend himself against in Grandstand Astro Wars?
3 What do electronic games need before they can work?
4 Electronic games cost a lot of money. If you saved your money, would you buy one or would you buy something else?

D **Something to talk about.**
1 Talk about one of the games that you have at home which you like to play.
2 Do you like games you can play with other people, or games you play by yourself?
3 Which are best, games you can learn quickly or games in which you can go on getting better?
4 Why do some people like electronic or television plug-in games?
5 Do you think that one day people will play electronic games and nothing else?

Make a finger puppet

How to make your puppet

1 Cut out a piece of stiff paper 8cm wide and about as long as your first finger. Divide it in half with a faint line longways and crossways.

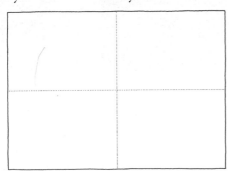

2 Draw the mouth in the middle. Put the eyes half-way above the mouth. Colour in the body as you like.

3 To make the nose, fold a piece of paper in half and cut out to fit between the eyes, like this.

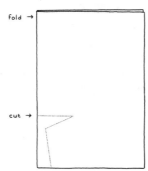

4 Fit the piece of paper round your finger and glue it (or fix with a pocket stapler) into a cylinder.

5 Cut a strip of paper with a hand at each end. Colour to match the body. Fix to the cylinder with glue or pocket stapler, like this.

6 Glue on the nose and make paper hair, a hat, ears or a tie as you like.

Here's what one puppet said to another puppet.

Puppet 1 I say, I say, I say. Why don't you get hungry in the Sahara Desert?

Puppet 2 I don't know. Why don't you get hungry in the Sahara Desert?

Puppet 1 You don't get hungry because of all the SAND WHICH IS THERE!

Puppet 2 I don't get it.

A Copy this 6 x 6 square grid and add two extra squares as shown. Complete the crossword using the clues given below.

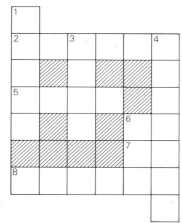

Across

2 You can make one to go on your finger.
5 '_____ in a manger.'
6 A lazy way to say 'thank you'.
7 When you play tag, you may be _____.
8 Did you make a puppet to go on your _____?

Down

1 Use a funny voice to make your puppet _____.
3 Make up a little _____ for your puppet to act.
4 A place where plays are put on.
6 Worn round the neck.

B Make a finger puppet to fit your own finger. Think of a name for your little puppet. Use a funny voice to make it speak. Think of a joke for your puppet to tell.

C Make another finger puppet and put one on each hand. Get the two puppets to talk to each other. Use a different voice for each one.

Here are some jokes you can try with your puppets. Can you think of some more?

Question: What did the biscuit say when the elephant trod on it?
Answer: Crumbs!

Question: What did the one-eyed man say to his wife when the elephant trod on his glass eye?
Answer: I haven't an idea (eye dear).

Question: What did the grape say when the elephant trod on it?
Answer: Nothing. It just gave a little whine.

D Work with your partner, or with your group. Make up a short concert or play for all the finger puppets to take part in.

Acknowledgements

The publishers would like to thank the following for permission to reproduce photos:
Ardea, p. 25; Aerofilms, p. 43; British Tourist Authority, p. 27; P Callow, p. 20; G. Duckworth, p. 38; Ian Fraser, pp. 10, 14, 44, 45; Syndication International, p. 3; J. Thomas, pp. 18, 47; John Topham, p. 35.

Illustrations are by Peter Bailey, Linda Birch, Patricia Capon, Peter Dennis, Terence Gabbey, David Hunt, John Hunt, Peter Joyce, Edward McLachlan, Duncan Larg, Annie Russell, Steve Wright.

Special thanks to Elmer Cotton sports shop and Selfridges, Oxford, for their assistance in setting up photographs.

Oxford University Press, Walton Street, Oxford OX2 6DP
Oxford New York Toronto
Delhi Bombay Calcutta Madras Karachi
Petaling Jaya Singapore Hong Kong Tokyo
Nairobi Dar es Salaam Cape Town
Melbourne Auckland

and associated companies in
Berlin Ibadan

Oxford is a trade mark of Oxford University Press

© Roderick Hunt 1983
First published 1983
Reprinted 1984, 1985, 1986, 1987, 1988 (twice)
ISBN 0 19 918173 X

Printed by Scotprint Ltd., Musselburgh